CLASSICS
Illustrated ®

Feodor Dostoyevsky
CRIME AND PUNISHMENT

essay by
Andrew J. Hoffman, Ph.D.
Brown University

ACCLAIM BOOKS
STUDY GUIDE

Crime and Punishment

art by Rudolph Palais

Classics Illustrated: Crime and Punishment
© Twin Circle Publishing Co.,
a division of Frawley Enterprises; licensed to First Classics, Inc.
All new material and compilation © 1997 by Acclaim Books, Inc.

Dale-Chall R.L.: 7.4

ISBN 1-57840-009-0

Acclaim Books, New York, NY
Printed in the United States

STUDY GUIDE

Crime and Punishment
by Dostoyevsky

OUR STORY BEGINS IN 19TH CENTURY RUSSIA. RASKOLNIKOV, A STUDENT RESIDING IN ST. PETERSBURG, IS CRUSHED BY POVERTY. HOPELESS AND FORLORN, HE HAS LOST ALL DESIRE TO DEAL WITH MATTERS OF PRACTICAL IMPORTANCE. STUBBORNLY, HE HAS REFUSED TO CONTINUE TO TUTOR YOUNG CHILDREN BECAUSE THE FEES WERE TOO MEAGER. HE IS DISHEARTENED... HE IS DESPERATE...

RASKOLNIKOV WAS HOPELESSLY IN DEBT TO HIS LANDLADY. HOUNDED BY POVERTY, HE FOOLISHLY PLANNED A MURDER TO SOLVE HIS PROBLEMS. HE DECIDED ON A REHEARSAL OF HIS PLAN.

I WANT TO ATTEMPT A THING LIKE *THAT* AND AM FRIGHTENED BY TRIFLES.

YES, MY HAT IS TOO NOTICEABLE. PEOPLE WOULD REMEMBER IT. AND THAT WOULD GIVE THEM A CLUE. IT'S JUST SUCH TRIFLES THAT ALWAYS RUIN EVERYTHING.

HEY THERE, GERMAN HATTER!

IF I AM SO SCARED NOW, WHAT WOULD IT BE IF IT CAME TO PASS THAT I WERE REALLY GOING TO DO IT?

RASKOLNIKOV ENTERED THE BUILDING AND STOPPED AT A FAMILIAR DOOR...

I AM RASKOLNIKOV, A STUDENT. I CAME HERE A MONTH AGO.

I REMEMBER, MY GOOD SIR..

SHE MISTRUSTS ME.

AND HERE I AM AGAIN ON THE SAME ERRAND.

STEP IN, MY GOOD SIR.

IT'S IN THE HOUSES OF SPITEFUL OLD WIDOWS THAT ONE FINDS SUCH CLEANLINESS.

WHAT DO YOU WANT?

I'VE BROUGHT SOMETHING TO PAWN.

BUT THE TIME IS UP FOR YOUR LAST PLEDGE. THE MONTH WAS UP THE DAY BEFORE YESTERDAY.

I WILL BRING YOU THE INTEREST FOR ANOTHER MONTH; WAIT A LITTLE WHILE.

BUT THAT'S FOR ME TO DO AS I PLEASE, MY GOOD SIR... TO WAIT OR TO SELL YOUR PLEDGE AT ONCE.

HOW MUCH WILL YOU GIVE ME FOR THE WATCH, ALYONA IVANOVNA?

IT'S SCARCELY WORTH ANYTHING. I GAVE YOU TWO RUBLES LAST TIME FOR YOUR RING AND ONE COULD BUY IT NEW FOR A RUBLE AND A HALF.

GIVE ME FOUR RUBLES FOR IT. I SHALL BE GETTING MONEY SOON.

A RUBLE AND A HALF AND INTEREST IN ADVANCE.

HAND IT OVER

SO, SHE CARRIES THE KEYS ALL IN ONE BUNCH ON A STEEL RING.

THERE'S ONE KEY THERE, THREE TIMES AS BIG AS ALL THE OTHERS. STRONGBOXES HAVE KEYS LIKE THAT.

I MAY BE BRINGING YOU SOMETHING ELSE IN A DAY OR TWO, ALYONA IVANOVNA... A VALUABLE THING... SILVER... A CIGARETTE BOX.

WE WILL TALK ABOUT IT THEN, SIR.

GOODBYE. ARE YOU ALWAYS AT HOME ALONE? YOUR SISTER IS NOT HERE WITH YOU?

WHAT BUSINESS IS SHE OF YOURS, MY GOOD SIR?

OH, NOTHING IN PARTICULAR, I SIMPLY ASKED. GOOD-DAY.

THE NEXT MORNING, HIS LANDLADY'S SERVANT WARNED RASKOLNIKOV OF HER MISTRESS' INTENTIONS.

PRASKOVYA PAVLOVNA MEANS TO COMPLAIN TO THE POLICE ABOUT YOU.

TO THE POLICE? WHAT DOES SHE WANT?

YOU DON'T PAY HER MONEY AND YOU WON'T TURN OUT OF THE ROOM. THAT IS WHAT SHE WANTS, TO BE SURE.

THAT WOULD NOT SUIT ME JUST NOW.

I'LL GO AND TALK TO HER TODAY.

ONE TIME YOU USED TO GO OUT TO TEACH CHILDREN. WHY IS IT YOU DO NOTHING NOW?

THEY PAY SO LITTLE FOR LESSONS. WHAT'S THE USE OF A FEW COPPERS?

AND YOU WANT TO GET A FORTUNE ALL AT ONCE?

YES, I WANT A FORTUNE!

LATER THAT DAY, IN THE MARKETPLACE, RASKOLNIKOV SPIED THE SISTER OF THE WOMAN HE PLANNED TO MURDER...

COME AROUND TOMORROW ABOUT SEVEN, LIZAVETA IVANOVNA.

TOMORROW?

UPON MY WORD, HOW FRIGHTENED YOU ARE OF ALYONA IVANOVNA, AND SHE IS NOTHING BUT YOUR STEP-SISTER.

JUST DON'T SAY A WORD TO HER COME AROUND TO US WITHOUT ASKING.

WHAT TIME AM I TO COME?

ABOUT SEVEN O'CLOCK!

AND WE'LL HAVE A CUP OF TEA.

THE OLD WOMAN WILL BE LEFT ALONE.

ALL RIGHT. I'LL COME.

RASKOLNIKOV DECIDED THE MOMENT HAD ARRIVED TO CARRY OUT HIS PLOT. HE FASHIONED A NOOSE FOR AN UNUSUAL PURPOSE... TO CARRY AN AXE.

HE SEWED THE NOOSE INTO HIS OVERCOAT UNDER THE ARMHOLE. THE HEAD OF THE AXE WOULD HANG IN THE NOOSE AND HE COULD GRIP THE HANDLE WITHOUT IT BEING NOTICEABLE, BY KEEPING HIS HAND IN HIS COAT POCKET.

HIS NEXT MOVE WAS TO WRAP WELL THE DUMMY CIGARETTE CASE. HE MUST WRAP IT TIGHTLY SO THAT THE OLD WOMAN WOULD HAVE TROUBLE UNTYING THE KNOT.

THE "CASE" WAS NOTHING MORE THAN A PIECE OF WOOD WITH A SMOOTH PIECE OF IRON ACROSS THE TOP TO GIVE IT WEIGHT.

I MUST HURRY. IT STRUCK SIX LONG AGO.

RASKOLNIKOV'S EVIL PLAN PROCEEDED SMOOTHLY. HE MET NO ONE WHO KNEW HIM AS HE ARRIVED AT THE PAWNBROKER'S HOUSE.

ONE FLAT ON THE SECOND FLOOR, BEING PAINTED, WAS WIDE OPEN BUT THE PAINTERS AT WORK DID NOT SEE HIM.

IT WOULD HAVE BEEN BETTER IF THEY HAD NOT BEEN HERE, BUT... IT'S TWO STORIES ABOVE THEM.

NO ANSWER. SHE'S HOME, OF COURSE... BUT SUSPICIOUS.

SHE IS LISTENING, TOO. I MUST BE CALM. I MUST RING THE BELL WITHOUT IMPATIENCE.

?

THE PAWNBROKER WAS FINALLY REASSURED BY HER VISITOR'S MANNER.

WHAT IS IT? WHO IS IT? WHAT DO YOU WANT?

WHY, ALYONA IVANOVNA, YOU KNOW ME... RASKOLNIKOV. I BROUGHT THE PLEDGE TO YOU I PROMISED THE OTHER DAY.

HOW PALE YOU ARE-- AND YOUR HANDS ARE TREMBLING.

FEVER. YOU CAN'T HELP GETTING PALE IF YOU'VE NOTHING TO EAT.

WHAT IS IT?

THE SILVER CIGARETTE CASE.

IT DOES NOT SEEM SOMEHOW LIKE SILVER. AND HOW YOU'VE WRAPPED IT!

THE PAWNBROKER TURNED TOWARD THE WINDOW TO INSPECT THE PLEDGE IN THE LIGHT.

WHAT HAS HE TIED IT UP LIKE THIS FOR

BENEATH THE VICTIM'S BED, THE MURDERER FOUND HER STRONGBOX.

THE MURDERER HEARD FOOTSTEPS IN THE NEXT ROOM. HE LOOKED IN AND SAW HIS VICTIM'S STEP-SISTER...

THE DEVIL. I MUST MAKE SURE OF HER.

RASKOLNIKOV MEANT TO LEAVE NO WITNESSES TO HIS CRIME.

I MUST FINISH HER AND GET AWAY FROM HERE.

HASTILY THE MURDERER WASHED THE AXE HANDLE TO ERASE THE BLOOD STAINS.

HE WAS INTERRUPTED BY A KNOCKING AT THE DOOR.

WHO CAN IT BE?

THE VISITOR POUNDED IMPATIENTLY ON THE DOOR.

HEY, ALYONA IVANOVNA, OLD WITCH! OPEN THE DOOR!

ASKOLNIKOV FASTENED THE LATCH AGAINST THE VISITOR WHO REFUSED TO LEAVE.

WHAT'S UP? ARE THEY ASLEEP OR MURDERED?

LIZAVETA IVANOVNA. HEY! OPEN THE DOOR!

HE MUST BE A PERSON OF AUTHORITY AND AN INTIMATE ACQUAINTANCE.

YOU DON'T SAY THERE'S NO ONE AT HOME, KOCH?

WHO THE DEVIL CAN TELL--IVE ALMOST BROKEN THE LOCK.

THAT'S QUEER. IVE COME ON BUSINESS.

AND I HAVE BUSINESS WITH HER, TOO.

WHAT CAN WE DO? I WAS HOPING TO GET SOME MONEY.

THE OLD WITCH HERSELF FIXED THE TIME FOR ME TO COME. SHE SITS HERE FROM YEAR'S END TO YEAR'S END, THE OLD HAG. HER LEGS ARE BAD AND YET HERE, ALL OF A SUDDEN, SHE IS OUT FOR A WALK.

I MUST GET RID OF THE AXE.

RASKOLNIKOV DESTROYED THE NOOSE WHICH HAD HELD THE AXE.

TORN PIECES OF LINEN COULDN'T AROUSE SUSPICION, WHATEVER HAPPENED. I THINK NOT, ANYWAY.

HE THEN RECALLED THAT THE PURSE HE CUT FROM THE PAWNBROKER'S NECK WAS STAINED WITH BLOOD.

THERE MUST BE BLOOD ON THE POCKET, TOO, FOR I PUT THE WET PURSE IN MY POCKET.

THE SOCK MUST SHOW TRACES OF BLOOD, TOO.

WHERE AM I TO PUT THE SOCK AND RAGS AND POCKET? THERE ARE NO MATCHES EVEN TO BURN THEM WITH. BETTER GO OUT AND THROW THEM ALL AWAY SOMEWHERE.

THE MURDERER FIRST HID HIS ILL-GOTTEN GAINS IN A HOLE IN THE WALL.

T T THAT MOMENT, THERE CAME A KNOCKING AT THE DOOR...

THAT'S THE PORTER'S VOICE. WHAT DOES HE WANT?

OPEN UP. ARE YOU DEAD OR ALIVE?

R ASKOLNIKOV HID THE LAST OF THE JEWELRY AND OPENED THE DOOR...

A SUMMONS FROM THE POLICE OFFICE.

THE POLICE? WHAT FOR?

WHAT DO THE POLICE WANT?

HOW CAN I TELL? YOU'RE SENT FOR, SO YOU GO.

THERE ARE STAINS BUT NOT VERY NOTICEABLE. ANYONE WHO HAD NO SUSPICION COULD DISTINGUISH NOTHING.

IT IS JUST AN ORDINARY SUMMONS. NO...IT'S A TRICK THEY WANT TO DECOY ME OUT THERE AND CONFOUND ME OVER EVERYTHING.

THE WORST PART OF IT IS, I'M ALMOST LIGHTHEADED...I MAY BLURT OUT SOMETHING STUPID.

ASSAILED BY FEARS THAT THE POLICE WOULD SOON BE SEARCHING HIS ROOM, RASKOLNIKOV DETERMINED THAT HE MUST FIND ANOTHER PLACE FOR HIS LOOT.

IN ANOTHER HALF-HOUR, ANOTHER QUARTER-HOUR, THEY MAY BE AFTER ME.

TO THE CANAL.

FEAR OF THE POLICE MADE THE STUDENT CONSIDER HIS PLANS.

FLING THEM INTO THE CANAL AND ALL TRACES WOULD BE HIDDEN IN THE WATER. THE THING WOULD BE AT AN END, BUT...

IT WOULD LOOK SUSPICIOUS FOR A MAN TO GO DOWN ON PURPOSE, STOP, AND THROW SOMETHING INTO THE WATER. AND WHAT IF THE JEWEL BOXES WERE TO FLOAT INSTEAD OF SINK?

CAN IT BE MY FANCY THAT EVERYONE SEEMS TO STARE AT ME?

DESPERATE FOR FEAR THAT HE WOULD BE CAUGHT BY THE POLICE WITH THE EVIDENCE OF HIS CRIME, THE STUDENT SOUGHT A PLACE TO HIDE HIS ILL-GOTTEN GAINS...

I HAVE BURIED MY TRACKS.

WHO CAN THINK OF LOOKING UNDER THAT STONE? AND IF THE JEWELS WERE FOUND, WHO WOULD THINK OF ME? IT IS ALL OVER. NO CLUE.

I DID NOT EVEN GLANCE INTO THE PURSE AND DON'T KNOW WHAT I HAD THERE, THAT FOR WHICH I HAVE UNDERGONE THESE AGONIES, AND HAVE DELIBERATELY UNDERTAKEN THIS FILTHY BUSINESS.

IT IS BECAUSE I AM VERY ILL. YESTERDAY AND THE DAY BEFORE AND ALL THIS TIME I HAVE BEEN WORRYING MYSELF. I SHALL GET WELL AND I SHALL NOT WORRY.

RASKOLNIKOV WAS INDEED ILL. HE WAS ON THE VERGE OF DELIRIUM FROM HIGH FEVER AS HE REACHED HIS HOME.

RASKOLNIKOV RECOVERED FROM HIS DELIRIUM TO FIND HIS STUDENT FRIEND RAZUMIHIN AT HIS SIDE.

IT'S A GOOD THING YOU'VE COME TO. FOR THE LAST FOUR DAYS YOU HAVE SCARCELY EATEN OR DRUNK ANYTHING. I BROUGHT ZAMETOV TO SEE YOU TWICE.

THE POLICE OFFICER? WHAT FOR?

BECAUSE WE ARE FRIENDS. WHAT ARE YOU SO UPSET ABOUT? HE WANTED TO MAKE YOUR ACQUAINTANCE BECAUSE I TALKED TO HIM A LOT ABOUT YOU. HE IS A CAPITAL FELLOW IN HIS OWN WAY.

YOU HAVE A VISITOR WITH MONEY FOR YOU. DON'T KEEP HIM WAITING.

MONEY?

35 RUBLES SENT BY YOUR MOTHER.

BRAVO; AND NOW, ARE YOU HUNGRY?

YES. IS THERE ANY SOUP?

SOME OF YESTERDAY'S, WITH POTATOES AND RICE. I'LL BRING IT AND SOME TEA.

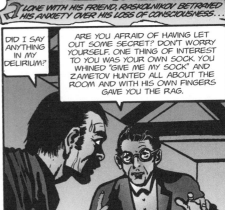

ALONE WITH HIS FRIEND, RASKOLNIKOV BETRAYED HIS ANXIETY OVER HIS LOSS OF CONSCIOUSNESS...

DID I SAY ANYTHING IN MY DELIRIUM?

ARE YOU AFRAID OF HAVING LET OUT SOME SECRET? DON'T WORRY YOURSELF. ONE THING OF INTEREST TO YOU WAS YOUR OWN SOCK. YOU WHINED "GIVE ME MY SOCK" AND ZAMETOV HUNTED ALL ABOUT THE ROOM AND WITH HIS OWN FINGERS GAVE YOU THE RAG.

JUST THEN, ANOTHER MAN ENTERED THE ROOM...

AH, DOCTOR ZOSSIMOV. YOU SEE, HE'S COME TO HIMSELF.

I SEE, I SEE; HAS HE EATEN ANYTHING?

I'VE GOT A PARTY TONIGHT; IT'S ONLY A STEP FROM HERE. COULDN'T HE COME? THERE WILL BE SOME SOME STUDENTS, A TEACHER NAMED ZAMETOV.

TELL ME WHAT YOU OR HE CAN HAVE IN COMMON WITH ZAMETOV. HE TAKES BRIBES.

WE REALLY HAVE SOMETHING IN COMMON. IT'S ALL ABOUT A HOUSE PAINTER. WE ARE GETTING HIM OUT OF A MESS.

A PAINTER?

YES, DOCTOR. HAVEN'T I TOLD YOU ABOUT THE MURDER OF THE OLD PAWNBROKER WOMAN? WELL, THE PAINTER IS MIXED UP IN IT.

OH, I HEARD ABOUT THAT MURDER BEFORE AND WAS INTERESTED IN IT... PARTLY... FOR ONE REASON. LIZAVETA WAS MURDERED, TOO.

YOU HEARD ABOUT IT. IT HAPPENED THE DAY BEFORE YOU FAINTED.

SOON AFTER THE MURDER, A SALOON KEEPER BROUGHT TO THE POLICE SOME GOLD EARRINGS. HE GOT THEM FROM A PAINTER WHO HAD BEEN WORKING IN THE HOUSE WHERE THE WOMAN WAS MURDERED. THE PAINTER CLAIMED TO HAVE FOUND THEM ON THE STREET IN FRONT OF THE HOUSE.

BEHIND THE DOOR? LYING BEHIND THE DOOR? BEHIND THE DOOR?

THE PAINTER, NIKOLAY, TOLD A LIE. HE FOUND THE EARRINGS BEHIND THE DOOR OF THE APARTMENT HE HAD BEEN PAINTING.

HE MUST HAVE WAKED FROM A DREAM.

IT IS MY BELIEF THAT THE REAL MURDERER DROPPED THOSE EARRINGS. HE WAS UPSTAIRS, LOCKED IN, WHEN KOCH AND PESTRYAKOV KNOCKED AT THE DOOR. THEY DID NOT STAY AT THE DOOR; SO THE MURDERER POPPED OUT AND RAN DOWN. HE HID IN THE FLAT WHEN THE PAINTERS, NIKOLAY AND DMITRI, LEFT IT.

NO, MY BOY, THAT'S TOO CLEVER. THAT BEATS EVERYTHING.

BECAUSE EVERYTHING FITS TOO WELL ...IT'S TOO MELODRAMATIC.

BUT WHY, WHY?

THE FOLLOWING DAY, THE STUDENT-MURDERER BOUGHT NEW CLOTHES, MOVED TO NEW LODGINGS AND DINED AT A FASHIONABLE RESTAURANT...

GIVE ME SOME TEA AND BRING ME THE PAPERS FOR THE LAST FIVE DAYS.

AH, HERE IT IS!

WHILE HE WAS READING, ZAMETOV CAME TO HIS TABLE...

YOU HERE? WHY RAZUMIHIN TOLD ME ONLY YESTERDAY YOU WERE UNCONSCIOUS. HOW STRANGE. DO YOU KNOW I'VE BEEN TO SEE YOU?

YES. YOU LOOKED FOR MY SOCK.

WHAT ARE YOU DOING, READING THE PAPERS ABOUT THE FIRES?

YOU'RE AWFULLY ANXIOUS TO KNOW WHAT I AM READING ABOUT.

NOT IN THE LEAST. I CAN'T HELP THINKING YOU ARE STILL SOMEWHAT DELIRIOUS.

I WAS SEARCHING- AND CAME HERE ON PURPOSE TO DO IT- FOR NEWS OF THE OLD PAWNBROKER WOMAN!

YOU ARE EITHER MAD, OR ...

OR? OR WHAT? WHAT? COME, TELL ME!

THE MURDERER SEEMS TO HAVE BEEN A DESPERATE FELLOW. HE RISKED EVERYTHING IN OPEN DAYLIGHT---BUT HIS HANDS SHOOK, TOO. HE DID NOT SUCCEED IN ROBBING THE PLACE; HE COULDN'T STAND IT. THAT WAS CLEAR FROM THE ...

WHY DON'T YOU CATCH HIM, THEN?

WE WILL. A MAN WILL COMMIT A CLEVER MURDER AND THEN HE GOES DRINKING IN A TAVERN. HE IS CAUGHT SPENDING MONEY. YOU WOULDN'T GO TO A TAVERN, OF COURSE?

YOU SEEM TO ENJOY THE SUBJECT AND WOULD LIKE TO KNOW HOW I SHOULD BEHAVE IF I MURDERED THE PAWNBROKER.

I SHOULD LIKE TO.

ALL RIGHT, THEN. I SHOULD HAVE TAKEN THE MONEY AND JEWELS. I SHOULD HAVE WALKED OUT OF THERE AND GONE STRAIGHT TO SOME DESERTED PLACE. I SHOULD HAVE LOOKED OUT BEFOREHAND SOME STONE WEIGHING A HUNDREDWEIGHT OR MORE. I WOULD LIFT THAT STONE AND PUT THE JEWELS AND MONEY IN THE HOLE.

BUT IS IT POSSIBLE?

OWN UP THAT YOU BELIEVED IT; YES YOU DID!

NOT A BIT OF IT. I BELIEVE IT LESS THAN EVER NOW.

SO YOU DID BELIEVE IT BEFORE, IF NOW YOU BELIEVE IT LESS THAN EVER?

SEE WHAT A LOT OF MONEY! RED NOTES AND BLUE, TWENTY-FIVE RUBLES. WHERE DID I GET THEM? AND WHERE DID MY NEW CLOTHES COME FROM? YOU KNOW I HAD NOT ONE KOPEK. YOU'VE CROSS EXAMINED MY LANDLADY, I'LL BE BOUND. WELL, THAT'S ENOUGH! TILL WE MEET AGAIN!

RASKOLNIKOV WAS FILLED WITH A LONGING TO SEE AGAIN THE SCENE OF HIS CRIME.

I WILL PRETEND I MEAN TO RENT THE APARTMENT.

WELL, WHAT DO YOU WANT? WHO ARE YOU?

I WANT TO RENT A FLAT. I'M LOOKING AROUND.

IT IS NOT THE TIME TO LOOK AT ROOMS AT NIGHT AND YOU OUGHT TO COME UP WITH THE PORTER.

THE FLOORS HAVE BEEN WASHED. WILL THEY BE PAINTED? IS THERE ANY BLOOD? THERE WAS A PERFECT POOL HERE.

ALARMED BY THE STRANGE VISITOR, THE PAINTERS MADE AN EXCUSE TO LEAVE THE APARTMENT. THEY ACCUSED RASKOLNIKOV TO THE PORTER OF THE HOUSE.

HE HAS BEEN TO LOOK AT THE FLAT.

WHICH FLAT?

WHERE WE WERE WORKING. 'WHY HAVE YOU WASHED AWAY THE BLOOD!' SAYS HE, AND 'THERE HAS BEEN A MURDER HERE,' SAYS HE.

WHO ARE YOU?

I AM RASKOLNIKOV, FORMERLY A STUDENT.

THE NEXT DAY, RASKOLNIKOV WAS PERSUADED BY RAZUMIHIN TO VISIT THE POLICE COURT TO PUT IN A CLAIM FOR THE ARTICLES HE HAD PAWNED WITH THE MURDERED PAWNBROKER.

YOU HAVE TO GIVE INFORMATION TO THE POLICE OF THE THINGS THAT BELONG TO YOU.

MR. PORFIRY, THE THINGS ARE ONLY WORTH ABOUT FIVE RUBLES, BUT I PRIZE THEM FOR THE SAKE OF THOSE FROM WHOM THEY CAME.

THAT'S WHY YOU BECAME EXCITED WHEN I MENTIONED THAT THE POLICE WERE INQUIRING FOR EVERYONE WHO HAD PLEDGES.

YOU SEEM TO BE JEERING AT ME! I DARE SAY, I MUST SEEM ABSURDLY ANXIOUS ABOUT SUCH TRASH BUT THE SILVER WATCH IS THE ONLY THING LEFT OF MY FATHER'S; IF MY MOTHER KNEW THE WATCH WAS LOST, SHE WOULD BE IN DESPAIR!

I DIDN'T MEAN THAT AT ALL.

YOUR THINGS WOULD NOT IN ANY CASE BE LOST. I HAVE BEEN EXPECTING YOU HERE FOR SOME TIME.

HE KNOWS.

YOUR THINGS WERE WRAPPED UP TOGETHER AND ON THE PAPER YOUR NAME WAS LEGIBLY WRITTEN, TOGETHER WITH THE DATE ON WHICH YOU LEFT THEM.

HOW OBSERVANT YOU ARE! I SUPPOSE THERE ARE A GREAT MANY PLEDGES.

YES, BUT WE KNOW ALL WHO HAD PLEDGES, AND YOU ARE THE ONLY ONE WHO HADN'T COME FORWARD.

I HAVEN'T BEEN QUITE WELL.

I HEARD THAT, TOO. YOU STILL LOOK PALE.

I AM QUITE WELL NOW, MR. PORFIRY.

IN MY ANGER I SHALL BETRAY MYSELF. WHY ARE THEY TORTURING ME?

REALLY DELIRIOUS? YOU DON'T SAY SO?

HE WAS UNCONSCIOUS AND DELIRIOUS TILL TODAY.

NONSENSE! DON'T YOU BELIEVE IT!

BUT HOW COULD YOU HAVE GONE OUT YESTERDAY IF YOU HADN'T BEEN DELIRIOUS? WHAT WAS THE OBJECT OF IT? AND ON THE SLY? WERE YOU IN YOUR SENSES WHEN YOU DID IT?

I WAS AWFULLY SICK OF MY FRIENDS YESTERDAY. ZAMETOV, THERE, SAW ME. WAS I SENSIBLE OR DELIRIOUS YESTERDAY, ZAMETOV?

IN MY OPINION, YOU TALKED SENSIBLY AND EVEN ARTFULLY; BUT YOU WERE EXTREMELY IRRITABLE.

THEY DON'T HIDE THAT THEY ARE TRACKING ME LIKE A PACK OF DOGS. THEY SIMPLY SPIT IN MY FACE. COME, STRIKE ME OPENLY; DON'T PLAY WITH ME LIKE A CAT WITH A MOUSE. AND WHAT IF IT'S ONLY MY FANCY?

IF YOU ONLY KNEW HOW YOU INTEREST ME. I AM REALLY GLAD YOU HAVE COME FORWARD AT LAST.

ARE THEY TRYING TO UPSET MY NERVES? WHY DID ZAMETOV ADD THAT I SPOKE ARTFULLY? EITHER IT'S ALL FANCY OR THEY KNOW. DO THEY KNOW ABOUT THE FLAT? DELIRIOUS INDEED. HA,HA,HA.

WHEN YOU CALLED ON THE PAWNBROKER, THE LAST TIME, IT WAS SEVEN O'CLOCK, WASN'T IT?

YES

DIDN'T YOU SEE, IN A FLAT THAT STOOD OPEN ON THE SECOND STORY, TWO WORKMAN, OR AT LEAST ONE OF THEM? THEY WERE PAINTING THERE. IT'S VERY IMPORTANT FOR THEM.

PAINTERS? NO, I DIDN'T SEE THEM, AND I DON'T THINK I SAW A FLAT OPEN.

THERE'S A TRAP HERE SOMEWHERE.

WHAT DO YOU MEAN? WHY, IT WAS ON THE DAY OF THE MURDER THE PAINTERS WERE AT WORK, AND HE WAS THERE THREE DAYS BEFORE. WHAT ARE YOU ASKING?

I KNEW IT. HE TRIED TO TRAP ME.

OF COURSE. EXCUSE ME. THIS BUSINESS IS TRYING MY BRAIN.

IT WOULD BE SUCH A GREAT THING FOR US TO FIND OUT IF ANYONE HAD SEEN THE PAINTERS BETWEEN SEVEN AND EIGHT, IN THE FLAT. I FANCIED YOU COULD HAVE TOLD US SOMETHING.

RASKOLNIKOV AND HIS FRIEND THEN LEFT THE PROSECUTING ATTORNEY'S OFFICE...

PORFIRY'S TONE WAS RATHER STRANGE; AND STILL MORE THAT WRETCH ZAMETOV. BUT WHY?

IF THEY HAD FACTS, I MEAN REAL FACTS, OR AT LEAST GROUNDS FOR SUSPICION...BUT THEY HAVE NO FACTS-- NOT ONE!

THE NEXT MORNING, ALARMED BY THE ACCUSATION OF HIS STRANGE VISITOR OF THE NIGHT BEFORE, RASKOLNIKOV BRAZENLY VISITED THE POLICE COURT TO CONFRONT THE PROSECUTING ATTORNEY, MR. PORFIRY.

MR. PORFIRY WILL SEE YOU SHORTLY.

THANK YOU.

HAS THE OLD MAN GIVEN HIS INFORMATION YET?

AH, MY DEAR GOOD FELLOW! COME SIT DOWN, OLD MAN... OR PERHAPS YOU DON'T LIKE TO BE CALLED "MY DEAR FELLOW" AND "OLD MAN?" PLEASE DON'T THINK IT TOO FAMILIAR.

I BROUGHT YOU THE PAPER... ABOUT THE WATCH.

NOTHING MORE IS NEEDED.

I BELIEVE YOU SAID YESTERDAY THAT YOU WOULD LIKE TO QUESTION ME... FORMALLY... ABOUT MY ACQUAINTANCE WITH THE MURDERED WOMAN.

THERE'S NO HURRY... NO HURRY... WE'VE PLENTY OF TIME.

I HAVE COME AND IF YOU HAVE ANYTHING TO ASK ME, ASK IT; AND IF NOT, ALLOW ME TO WITHDRAW!

WHAT SHALL I QUESTION YOU ABOUT? I LOOK UPON YOU SIMPLY AS A VISITOR.

I BELIEVE IT'S A LEGAL TRADITION FOR ALL INVESTIGATING LAWYERS TO BEGIN THEIR ATTACK WITH AN IRRELEVANT SUBJECT, SO AS TO DIVERT THE MAN THEY ARE CROSS-EXAMINING. ISN'T THAT SO?

DOES HE REALLY WANT TO DISTRACT MY ATTENTION WITH HIS SILLY BABBLE?

I ASSURE YOU, THESE INTERROGATIONS ARE SOMETIMES MORE EMBARRASSING FOR THE INTERROGATOR THAN FOR THE INTERROGATED.

YOU ARE CERTAINLY QUITE RIGHT IN LAUGHING AT OUR LEGAL FORMS. SOME OF THESE PSYCHOLOGICAL METHODS ARE EXCEEDINGLY RIDICULOUS AND PERHAPS USELESS. YOU ARE STUDYING FOR THE LAW, ARE YOU NOT?

I WAS...

WELL, THEN, IT IS A PRECEDENT FOR YOU FOR THE FUTURE. IF I SUSPECT THIS MAN OR THAT FOR A CRIMINAL, WHY SHOULD I WORRY HIM PREMATURELY, EVEN THOUGH I HAD EVIDENCE AGAINST HIM?

IN ONE CASE, I MAY BE BOUND TO ARREST A MAN AT ONCE; BUT ANOTHER MAY BE IN QUITE A DIFFERENT POSITION. SO WHY SHOULDN'T I LET HIM WALK ABOUT THE TOWN A BIT?

IF I SHUT A MAN UP TOO SOON, I MAY DEPRIVE MYSELF OF THE MEANS OF SETTING FURTHER EVIDENCE AGAINST HIM. A CULTIVATED MAN IS PSYCHOLOGICALLY UNABLE TO ESCAPE ME. HAVE YOU SEEN A MOTH AROUND A CANDLE? THAT'S HOW HE WILL KEEP CIRCLING AROUND ME. FREEDOM WILL LOSE ITS ATTRACTION BEFORE LONG.

THIS IS BEYOND THE CAT PLAYING WITH A MOUSE LIKE YESTERDAY. HE WANTS TO MAKE ME LOSE MY HEAD BUT I WON'T DO IT.

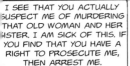

I SEE THAT YOU ACTUALLY SUSPECT ME OF MURDERING THAT OLD WOMAN AND HER SISTER. I AM SICK OF THIS. IF YOU FIND THAT YOU HAVE A RIGHT TO PROSECUTE ME, THEN ARREST ME.

GOOD HEAVENS, YOU'RE ILL! MY DEAR FELLOW, YOU'LL DRIVE YOURSELF OUT OF YOUR MIND!

YOU'RE FULL OF INDIGNATION AT THE WRONGS YOU'VE RECEIVED. FIRST FROM DESTINY, THEN FROM THE POLICE OFFICERS. THAT'S SO, ISN'T IT? I KNOW HOW YOU WENT TO TAKE A FLAT AT NIGHT AND ASKED ABOUT THE BLOOD...YOU WERE DELIRIOUS WHEN YOU DID ALL THIS.

HE IS STILL LYING...TRYING TO TRAP ME.

I WAS NOT DELIRIOUS. I WAS QUITE MYSELF. DO YOU UNDERSTAND?

YES, I UNDERSTAND. IF YOU WERE ACTUALLY A CRIMINAL, YOU CERTAINLY OUGHT TO INSIST THAT YOU WERE DELIRIOUS. THAT'S SO, ISN'T IT?

YOU ARE LYING. YOU ARE LYING AND MOCKING SO THAT I MAY BETRAY MYSELF TO YOU!.

WHY, MY DEAR MAN, YOU COULD NOT BETRAY YOURSELF ANY FURTHER. YOU ARE IN A PASSION. DON'T SHOUT; I SHALL CALL THE CLERKS.

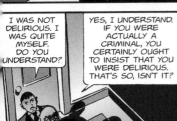

YOU KEEP TELLING LIES. YOU WANT TO FRIGHTEN ME...OR YOU ARE SIMPLY LAUGHING AT ME.

WHAT A WILY PERSON YOU ARE. THERE'S NO CATCHING YOU. I HAVE A SINCERE LIKING FOR YOU AND GENUINELY WISH YOU GOOD.

MY DEAR RASKOLNIKOV, EXCUSE ME; I'M AFRAID YOU MUST GO. YOU SEE, WHAT A SURPRISE. GOOD-BYE.

I SUPPOSE YOU DIDN'T EXPECT IT?

YOU DID NOT EXPECT IT, EITHER, MY FRIEND. SEE HOW YOUR HAND IS TREMBLING.

YOU'RE TREMBLING, TOO, PORFIRY.

YES, I DIDN'T EXPECT IT. BUT YOUR TEETH ARE CHATTERING YOU ARE AN IRONICAL PERSON. COME, TILL WE MEET!

I DON'T KNOW WHAT TO WISH YOU. I SHOULD LIKE TO WISH YOU SUCCESS, BUT YOUR OFFICE IS SUCH A COMICAL ONE.

WHY COMICAL?

WHY, HOW LONG YOU MUST HAVE TORTURED AND HARASSED THAT POOR NIKOLAY, PSYCHOLOGICALLY, UNTIL HE CONFESSED. YOU MUST HAVE BEEN AT HIM NIGHT AND DAY. AND NOW THAT HE HAS CONFESSED, YOU'LL BE VIVISECTING HIM AGAIN. "YOU ARE LYING," YOU'LL SAY, "YOU ARE NOT THE MURDERER, YOU CAN'T BE!"

YOU ARE QUICK-WITTED. YOU NOTICED THAT I SAID TO NIKOLAY IT WAS NOT HIS OWN TALE HE WAS TELLING. I SHALL LOOK FORWARD TO MEETING YOU AGAIN.

SO SHALL I

RASKOLNIKOV KNEW THAT ONCE THE FALSEHOOD OF NIKOLAY'S CONFESSION WAS AN ACTUAL FACT, THEY WOULD BE AFTER HIM AGAIN. TILL THEN, AT LEAST, HE WAS FREE, AND MUST DO SOMETHING FOR HIMSELF FOR THE DANGER WAS IMMINENT. BUT HOW IMMINENT? WHAT HAD PORFIRY BEEN TRYING TO GET AT?

A FEW DAYS LATER, RASKOLNIKOV HAD A VISITOR. IT WAS HIS FRIEND, RAZUMIHIN...

PLEASE DON'T THINK I'VE COME TO ASK YOU QUESTIONS. I HAVE ONLY COME TO FIND OUT ONCE AND FOR ALL WHETHER OR NOT YOU ARE MAD. THERE IS A CONVICTION IN THE AIR THAT YOU ARE MAD, OR NEARLY SO.

YOU HAVE NOT SAID A WORD TO ME AS YET. YOU ARE NOT MAD... THAT I'D SWEAR. BUT THERE'S SOME SECRET, AND I DON'T INTEND TO WORRY MY BRAINS OVER YOUR SECRETS, AND I KNOW WHAT TO DO NOW.

WHAT DO YOU MEAN TO DO NOW?

WHAT BUSINESS IS IT OF YOURS WHAT I MEAN TO DO?

YOU ARE GOING IN FOR A DRINKING BOUT.

HE'S A POLITICAL CONSPIRATOR. HE MUST BE. IT CAN ONLY BE THAT.

OH, BY THE WAY, DO YOU REMEMBER THE MURDER... YOU KNOW, THAT OLD WOMAN? THE MURDERER HAS BEEN FOUND. IT'S ONE OF THE PAINTERS.

TELL ME, PLEASE, FROM WHOM YOU HEARD THAT, AND WHY DOES IT INTEREST YOU SO?

I HEARD IT FROM PORFIRY.

WHAT DID PORFIRY SAY?

HE GAVE ME A CAPITAL EXPLANATION OF IT, PSYCHOLOGICALLY, AFTER HIS FASHION.

HE EXPLAINED IT? EXPLAINED IT HIMSELF?

YES, YES. I'LL TELL YOU ALL ABOUT IT ANOTHER TIME. YOU KNOW, THERE WAS A TIME I FANCIED... BUT NO MATTER, ANOTHER TIME. GOODBYE. I'LL COME AGAIN VERY SOON.

HE'S A POLITICAL CONSPIRATOR, THERE'S NOT A DOUBT ABOUT IT. AND I WAS ALMOST THINKING... GOOD HEAVENS, WHAT I THOUGHT. I WRONGED HIM. WHAT A VILE IDEA ON MY PART. NIKOLAY IS A BRICK FOR CONFESSING. AND HOW CLEAR IT ALL IS NOW.

I WILL ESCAPE AFTER ALL. PORFIRY HIMSELF HAS ACCEPTED NIKOLAY'S CONFESSION. OH, TO THINK THAT RAZUMIHIN HAD BEGUN TO SUSPECT ME.

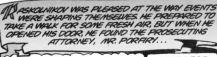

RASKOLNIKOV WAS PLEASED AT THE WAY EVENTS WERE SHAPING THEMSELVES. HE PREPARED TO TAKE A WALK FOR SOME FRESH AIR, BUT WHEN HE OPENED HIS DOOR, HE FOUND THE PROSECUTING ATTORNEY, MR. PORFIRY...

PERHAPS THIS WILL MEAN THE END. COULD HE HAVE BEEN LISTENING AT THE DOOR? HOW COULD HE HAVE APPROACHED SO QUIETLY?

SORRY FOR INTRUDING LIKE THIS. I WAS PASSING BY, AND THOUGHT I'D STOP BY FOR FIVE MINUTES.

AH, THESE CIGARETTES; THEY ARE WICKED, POSITIVELY WICKED. YET I CAN'T GIVE THEM UP.

HE'S PLAYING HIS PROFESSIONAL TRICKS AGAIN.

I CAME TO SEE YOU DAY BEFORE YESTERDAY, IN THE EVENING. I CAME INTO THIS VERY ROOM. DON'T YOU LOCK YOUR DOOR?

I'VE COME TO HAVE IT OUT WITH YOU. A STRANGE SCENE PASSED BETWEEN US LAST TIME WE MET. DO YOU REMEMBER HOW WE PARTED? YOUR NERVES WERE UNHINGED AND YOUR KNEES WERE SHAKING, AND SO WERE MINE.

WHAT IS HE UP TO? WHAT DOES HE TAKE ME FOR?

I'VE DECIDED OPENNESS IS BETTER BETWEEN US. YES, SUCH SUSPICIONS AND SUCH SCENES CANNOT CONTINUE FOR LONG. NIKOLAY PUT A STOP TO IT OR I DON'T KNOW WHAT WE MIGHT HAVE COME TO.

WHAT ARE YOU DRIVING AT NOW?

I CONSIDER IT MY DUTY TO EXPLAIN MYSELF. I'VE CAUSED YOU A GREAT DEAL OF SUFFERING. I UNDERSTAND WHAT IT MUST MEAN FOR A MAN WHO HAS BEEN UNFORTUNATE, BUT WHO IS PROUD AND, ABOVE ALL, IMPATIENT, TO HAVE TO BEAR SUCH TREATMENT.

DOES HE REALLY BELIEVE ME INNOCENT?

IT'S SCARCELY NECESSARY TO GO OVER DETAILS. MY SUSPICIONS WERE AROUSED BY A COMPLETE ACCIDENT. WHAT IS IT? I BELIEVE THERE IS NO NEED TO GO INTO THAT. I WAS THE FIRST TO PITCH ON TO YOU. DO YOU SUPPOSE I DIDN'T COME TO SEARCH YOUR ROOM AT THE TIME? I DID. I WAS THERE WHEN YOU WERE LYING ILL, NOT IN MY OWN PERSON, BUT I WAS THERE. YOUR ROOM WAS SEARCHED TO THE LAST THREAD AT THE FIRST SUSPICION...

I THOUGHT TO MYSELF, IF HE'S GUILTY, HE'S SURE TO COME OF HIS OWN ACCORD. ANOTHER MAN WOULDN'T BUT HE WILL. YOU REMEMBER MR. RAZUMIHIN DISCUSSING THE SUBJECT WITH YOU? WE WANTED TO EXCITE YOU, SO WE SPREAD RUMORS THAT HE MIGHT DISCUSS THE CASE WITH YOU.

DO YOU REMEMBER THE OLD MAN WHO CALLED YOU A MURDERER TO YOUR FACE? WE PLANTED HIM I WOULD HAVE GIVEN A THOUSAND RUBLES AT THAT MOMENT TO HAVE SEEN YOU WITH MY OWN EYES.

THE MURDERER COMMITTED THIS CRIME FOR A THEORY. HE COMMITTED THE MURDER AND COULDN'T TAKE THE MONEY. HE DID MANAGE TO HIDE IT UNDER A STONE. THAT MUCH WE KNOW.

IT WASN'T ENOUGH FOR HIM TO SUFFER AGONY BEHIND THE DOOR WHILE VISITORS BATTERED AT IT AND RANG THE BELL; NO, HE HAD TO RETURN TO HIS EMPTY LODGING, HALF DELIRIOUS, TO RECALL THE BELL RINGING. HE WANTED TO FEEL THE COLD SHIVER OVER AGAIN.

THEN... WHO THEN... IS THE MURDERER?

WHY, YOU, MY DEAR FELLOW. YOU ARE THE MURDERER

I CAME ON PURPOSE TO TELL YOU EVERYTHING AND DEAL OPENLY WITH YOU.

IT WAS NOT I WHO MURDERED HER!

IT WAS YOU. AND NO ONE ELSE.

IF SO, WHAT DID YOU COME HERE FOR? I ASK YOU THE SAME QUESTION AGAIN: IF YOU CONSIDER ME GUILTY, WHY DON'T YOU TAKE ME TO PRISON?

I WILL ANSWER YOU. IN THE FIRST PLACE, TO ARREST YOU DIRECTLY IS NOT TO MY INTEREST.

HOW SO, IF YOU ARE CONVINCED I AM THE MURDERER?

WELL, FRANKLY, IT WON'T BE TO MY ADVANTAGE. SECONDLY, I'VE COME TO YOU BECAUSE I CONSIDER I OWE YOU AN EXPLANATION. I DON'T WANT YOU TO LOOK ON ME AS A MONSTER AND IN THE THIRD PLACE, I'VE COME TO YOU SO THAT YOU SHOULD SURRENDER AND CONFESS.

LISTEN, PORFIRY. YOU HAVE NOTHING BUT PSYCHOLOGY TO GO ON. WELL, WHAT IF YOU ARE MISTAKEN?

I AM NOT MISTAKEN. I HAVE A LITTLE FACT TO GO ON.

WHAT LITTLE FACT?

I WON'T TELL YOU THAT.

YOU HAVEN'T TOLD ME THE ADVANTAGE IT WOULD BE FOR ME TO CONFESS.

DON'T YOU KNOW HOW IT WOULD LESSEN YOUR SENTENCE? YOU WOULD BE CONFESSING AT A MOMENT WHEN ANOTHER MAN HAS TAKEN THE CRIME ON HIMSELF AND HAS MUDDLED THE WHOLE CASE.

I WILL ARRANGE FOR YOUR CONFESSION SO THAT IT SHALL COME AS A COMPLETE SURPRISE. YOUR CRIME WILL APPEAR TO HAVE BEEN THE WORK OF A MADMAN. I AM AN HONEST MAN, RASKOLNIKOV, AND WILL KEEP MY WORD.

I DON'T CARE ABOUT LESSENING THE SENTENCE.

COME, WHAT DOES IT MATTER THAT YOU WILL PASS INTO ANOTHER CLASS OF MEN; WHAT OF IT THAT, PERHAPS, NO ONE WILL SEE YOU FOR SO LONG A TIME?

WHEN DO YOU MEAN TO ARREST ME?

OH, I CAN LET YOU WALK ABOUT ANOTHER DAY OR TWO. THINK IT OVER, MY DEAR FELLOW, AND PRAY.

AND WHAT IF I RUN AWAY?

NO, YOU WON'T RUN AWAY. A PEASANT WOULD RUN AWAY, BUT NOT YOU.

I HAVE ONE REQUEST TO MAKE BEFORE I LEAVE. IN CASE YOU ARE TAKEN WITH THE NOTION OF COMMITTING SUICIDE, DO LEAVE A NOTE AND MENTION THE STONE UNDER WHICH YOU HID THE MONEY.

ORFIRY'S VISIT STIRRED THE MURDER'S EMOTIONS. HIS CONSCIENCE TROUBLED RASKOLNIKOV AS HE WALKED BESIDE THE NEVA RIVER

IN ANOTHER WEEK, ANOTHER MONTH, I SHALL BE DRIVEN IN A PRISON VAN ACROSS THIS BRIDGE. I SHOULD LIKE TO REMEMBER THIS. WHAT SHALL I BE FEELING AND THINKING THEN?

THERE'S A PEASANT WOMAN WITH A BABY, BEGGING. IT'S CURIOUS THAT SHE THINKS ME HAPPIER THAN HERSELF.

BLESS YOU SIR, BLESS YOU.

SUDDENLY, RASKOLNIKOV WAS OVERCOME BY HIS CONSCIENCE AND HE FOLLOWED ITS COMMAND...

BOW DOWN TO THE PEOPLE, KISS THE EARTH, FOR YOU HAVE SINNED AGAINST IT; SAY TO THE WHOLE WORLD, "I AM A MURDERER."

HE'S DRUNK!

HE'S GOING TO JERUSALEM, BROTHERS, AND SAYING GOODBYE TO HIS CHILDREN AND TO HIS COUNTRY.

QUITE A YOUNG MAN, TOO. AND A GENTLEMAN.

IS CONSCIENCE RELENTLESSLY DROVE RASKOLNIKOV TO THE POLICE COURT...

HELLO! WHAT'S THE MATTER?

YOU ARE FEELING ILL. HERE, SIT DOWN. I'LL GET YOU SOME WATER.

DRINK SOME WATER. YOU'LL FEEL BETTER.

IT WAS I...

IT WAS I WHO KILLED THE OLD PAWNBROKER WOMAN AND HER SISTER WITH AN AXE AND ROBBED THEM!

THIS THEN WAS THE STORY OF THE INTELLIGENT YOUNG MAN WHO COMMITTED A PREMEDITATED, "PERFECT CRIME." HIS OWN CONSCIENCE AND THE EFFORTS OF A BRILLIANT POLICE ATTORNEY BROUGHT ABOUT THE DRAMATIC CONFESSION AND A JUST PUNISHMENT. RASKOLNIKOV WAS SENTENCED TO SERVE A LONG TERM AT HARD LABOR IN A SIBERIAN PRISON.

CRIME & PUNISHMENT
FEODOR DOSTOYEVSKY

A ground-breaking novel of psychological insight, Dostoyevsky's *Crime and Punishment* has remained one of the world's most treasured works since its publication in 1864. Though the story of Rodion Romanovich Raskolnikov's brutal double-murder and the torturous guilt following are the most memorable and compelling parts of the book, without the surrounding stories of Raskolnikov's mother and sister, the hapless Marmeladov family he befriends, the cruel manipulations of two wretched men, and the loving kindness of his friend Razumihin, the novel has little to offer beyond the thoughts and actions of a madman. With these other pieces, we can not only see what has precipitated Raskolnikov's madness, but also his efforts to rise above his madness and the oppressive restrictions of his society. Instead of a detective story, ending with the just imprisonment of the criminal, the book becomes a narrative of redemption, with Raskolnikov's discovery of the true freedom in the human soul.

The Author

Born in 1821, Feodor Mikhailovich Dostoyevsky came from a distinguished, nearly noble family. Though his ancestors had been awarded lands and titles in Lithuania two centuries before his birth, by the time Dostoyevsky was born, most men in his family worked either as priests or professionals. His father was a military physician, by all accounts miserly and dictatorial. The family lived on the grounds of the government hospital his father ran. Feodor, the second child of seven, while fortunate by the general standard of life in 19th-century Russia, lived in his own family like a subject of an oppressive king. He and his older brother Mikhail became very close as a defense against this difficult life.

When he was nine, the family took control of a large parcel of land called Darovoe, and Feodor Dostoyevsky had a break every summer from his father's stern control. Before the serfs were freed by Czar Alexander II more than thirty years later, the *barin*, or landlord,

enjoyed almost complete control over the fate of the people who lived on his property. In the case of Darovoe these *muzhin*, or serfs, numbered over a thousand. The doctor seldom come to Darovoe, so Feodor, his siblings, the nurses and servants, and his mother could spend their summers as they pleased. Feodor preferred spending his time among the muzhin.

These summer breaks did not last many years. Dostoyevsky's mother fell ill with tuberculosis and died during the winter of 1836, when Feodor was just 15 years old. His father quickly resolved to send his two oldest sons to St. Petersburg, where they would study for admission to the college of military engineering; a graduate from this prestigious institution could then choose between a career in the military or one as an engineer. Neither career appealed to the brothers, who preferred literature, but their father controlled their lives by denying them money for any studies of which he did not approve. The threat of poverty gave way to the real thing within a few short years. Their father, troubled by his wife's death, began to drink to excess,

sleep with his servants, and cruelly abuse his serfs. In retaliation, the serfs conspired to eliminate their bad master, and in 1839 they murdered him. The brothers now had no choice but to continue their studies: the Russian state, which essentially became their guardian, honored the dead father's plans for his sons regardless of their wishes. Though Feodor had modest success at the academy, he thrived only with a pen in his hand.

He began to conceive of himself as a genius, the next Gogol (one of the most popular 19th century Russian writers) only waiting to be discovered. This discovery took place much earlier than Dostoyevsky could have hoped. Not long after completing his schooling, he wrote a novel, *Poor Folk*, based on the muzhin he had known at Darovoe. Friends brought the manuscript to the attention of the era's most influential critics, who celebrated the appearance of the talented twenty-three-year-old. Even before the publication of his first book, Dostoyevsky was popular among Russia's literati. But his very popularity ruined him: under constant pressure to write, he hurried his work, producing several novels of uneven quality in only three years. Bragging of his own genius, playing at revolution, Dostoyevsky began to cut a ridiculous figure on the St. Petersburg literary scene. He fell into quarrels with people who would have happily helped him, and as quickly as he had become the most promising writer of his generation he became the most laughable. There was more trouble in store: the pace of his work, combined with the stresses of his liberal political associations and new-found social whirl, brought on his first epileptic fits.

The laughing stopped in 1849 when Dostoyevsky and two dozen others were arrested for revolutionary plotting. Most of Europe had exploded with socialist fervor the year before, and Czar Nicholas I had no intention of allowing anything to disturb his empire. He planned to teach these rabble-rousers, and any others who might still be lurking, an unforgettable lesson.

Dostoyevsky and the other conspirators were marched into a courtyard, sentenced to death, and lined up before a firing squad. But the soldiers did not fire. The convicts were told that the Czar had changed his mind and commuted their sentence to hard labor in Siberia. Dostoyevsky was sentenced to four years in prison, to be followed by four years at a Siberian Army outpost.

In prison, Dostoyevsky was in an odd position. As a gentleman and man of letters, he received some special treatment, though not enough to lessen the wretched and painful conditions of his imprisonment. On the other hand, other prisoners regarded him more as a pampered boy than a man. Allowed only a Bible and rare letters from his family, Dostoyevsky fell under the influence of his fellow prisoners. Where once he might have been a "gentleman revolutionary," content to sit in St. Petersburg cafés sipping tea and discussing violent overthrow of the Czar, now he embraced his fellow prisoners' twin beliefs in the saving strength of the Russian people and in Christian redemption which could only be attained through suffering. In particular, he came to believe that the suffering of the muzhin would eventually produce redemption not only for the serfs, but for all of Russia.

Sent to serve the remainder of his sentence in a desert outpost called Semipaltinsk, Dostoyevsky stirred up a mixture of good luck and bad choices. Within a year, he was befriended by the young Baron Wrangel; the two became inseparable friends. One of the things that bound them was unrequited passions for unattainable women. For Dostoyevsky, the woman was Maria Isaev, the wife of a school master who had been dismissed from his post for drinking. He liked the husband and the Isaevs' son Pavel, but he fell passionately in love with Maria. After two years of a deep but unconsummated love, Maria moved when her husband found a post hundreds of miles away. Separated indefinitely, the two wrote letters to one another until Maria sent word that her husband had died. Now Maria herself was stricken with tuberculosis; with nowhere else to turn, she agreed to marry Dostoyevsky.

The new family soon returned to St. Petersburg. There, taking advantage of the liberalization of the press under the new Czar, Alexander I, Dostoyevsky and his brother started a new magazine. Forced to write quickly for his magazine, his return to the literary trade seemed to pick up just where he had left off more than a decade before, with a series of unspectacular stories and novels. The exception was *The House of the Dead*, which told of his years in the Siberian prison; unfortunately, by the time the book was published, reforms had already begun. These social changes occurred in spasms, and sometimes, between reforms, the censors would close down the brothers' magazine. Nervous, physically ruined by his imprisonment and his repeated epileptic seizures, and emotionally battered by his unhappy marriage to Maria and an affair with a younger writer, Polina Suslova, Dostoyevsky escaped to Europe. He returned only when his wife began her decline into death. He sat by her through a long winter, writing *Notes from the Underground*, waiting for her release. Within a few months of Maria's death his brother Mikhail also died, leaving Dostoyevsky with a mountain of debt for their magazine, and with responsibility for his stepson, his brother's widow, and his nieces and nephews. Barely able to face these burdens, he retired again to Europe,

HE'S A POLITICAL CONSPIRATOR, THERE'S NOT A DOUBT ABOUT IT. AND I WAS ALMOST THINKING... GOOD HEAVENS, WHAT I THOUGHT. I WRONGED HIM. WHAT A VILE IDEA ON MY PART. NIKOLAY IS A BRICK FOR CONFESSING. AND HOW CLEAR IT ALL IS NOW.

this time with Suslova. But by this time their relationship had changed: she wanted him with her, but refused to sleep with him. Dostoyevsky vented his frustration at the roulette table, gambling away everything he had, putting himself ever deeper into debt. He soon found himself alone, in Germany, unable to pay for his room, reduced to pawning his clothes. He began *Crime and Punishment,* reaching into the darkest depths of his soul and emerging with a version of himself at twenty-two: Raskolnikov. Back in Russia, the publication of the first portion of the book in a magazine earned him sudden fame. This was the book which

Brutality, Russia and Dreams

After his mother's death, when Dostoyevsky's father sent him off to school, Feodor and his brother Mikhail took a long unpleasant journey to St. Petersburg. Along the way, they stopped at an inn. While they were waiting there, a government courier, a high official, swaggered in. He gulped down some food while his tired horse was switched for a fresh one, then hopped into the carriage behind the new driver and horse. At once, the courier began pummeling the driver on his neck and head. Each time the official struck the driver, the driver raised his whip against the horse.

Dostoyevsky watched this strange sight until the carriage disappeared down the road: the official beating the driver, the driver beating the horse, the horse running hard to escape.

In this episode, Dostoyevsky saw all that had oppressed Russia, and all that had oppressed him. The cruel government official, unrestrained in his use of power, could whip the driver all he liked. The driver, unable to retaliate

against his oppressor, practiced the same cruelty on the helpless horse. It took Dostoyevsky many years to see how his father's treatment of him had made him cruel and reckless, and he only discovered it through a dream.

This was not a dream he dreamed, but one he wrote. In *Crime and Punishment,* just before Raskolnikov goes out to kill the old pawnbroker, he has a dream. He's a outside a tavern. A rough peasant emerges, drunk, encouraging everyone around him to pile into his wagon. "She'll pull everybody!" he vows about his old mare. "I'll whip her to death!" But the horse cannot move the overloaded cart. The peasant begins to beat the horse with a stick. When on lookers object, he says it's his horse and he can treat her as he likes. Some of the drunken crowd and rowdy boys join in, until they have at last pulverized the poor mare. In the dream, Raskolnikov is just a boy and is overwhelmed with sympathy for the horse. He wakes sweating and asks himself, "Can it be that I will really take an axe and hit her on the head and smash her skull? I couldn't endure it!" And yet he does it, proving to himself—and to Dostoyevsky—that the cruelty he had experienced had entered into him and would not cease until he had found a way to reverse it.

realized the talent promised in his first novel. Now, at forty-four, broke and broken, Dostoyevsky had reached the very edge of greatness.

He still had one major problem: to escape the debt from his joint venture with his brother, he had signed a suicidal contract, selling all of his previous work for a pittance and promising a new novel by November 1, 1866. If he failed to deliver the manuscript, he would forfeit the rights to all his future work. A month before the deadline, he had not written a single line. A friend hired a young stenographer, Anna Snitkin, and in a month Dostoyevsky had dictated *The Gambler*, based on his experience with Polina Suslova. In the process, he and Anna fell in love. He had fame, release from his villainous contract, and a new marriage to a girl half his age all at once. Though it took several years and a return to Russia, Dostoyevsky eventually achieved a moderate level of wealth as well. Anna became his dedicated protector and business manager, as well as mother to their four children.

Back in Russia, Dostoyevsky alternated between editing magazines — the right-wing journal *The Citizen* and his own *A Writer's Diary* — and writing his own books, most notably *The Idiot*, *The Possessed*, and *The Brothers Karamazov*. He continued to be a controversial figure; his politics had gone from stridently liberal to deeply conservative and the autobiographical nature of his fiction always made his readers wonder which of the depraved characters about whom he wrote was closest to the real man. When he died at fifty-nine in January 1881, his health compromised by epilepsy, imprisonment and his years of poverty, he was the most passionately beloved of all the great Russian men of letters.

THE MURDERER FIRST HID HIS ILL-GOTTEN GAINS IN A HOLE IN THE WALL.

THE MURDER PLOT

Rodion Romanovich Raskolnikov (Rodya, Rodka)
an impoverished college student, insane but not delusional

Alyona Ivanovna
a pawnbroker to whom Raskolnikov owes money

Lizaveta Ivanovna
a rag merchant, the pawnbroker's much younger half-sister

Praskovya Pavlovna (Pashenka)
Raskolnikov's landlady, to whose now-dead daughter Raskolnikov was engaged and to whom he owes money

Nastasya
the landlady's kindly servant girl

Dmitri Prokofych Razumihin
Raskolnikov's college friend

Nikodim Fomich
the police chief

Alexander Gregorievich Zametov
a police clerk and friend of Razumihin

Ilya Petrovich (Gunpowder)
the police chief's assistant, an excitable man

Porfiry Petrovich
a police inspector and distant relative of Razumihin

Nikolay Koch and Mitka Pestryakov
painters, they were working in the pawnbroker's building when the murder took place; Koch eventually confesses to the crime

Zossimov
the doctor, a friend of Razumihin

THE RASKOLNIKOV FAMILY PLOT

Pulcheria Alexandrovna Raskolnikov
Raskolnikov's mother

Avdotya Romanova (Dunya, Dunechka)
his sister

Arkady Ivanovich Svidrigailov
a country squire, a thorough scoundrel, who tries to force himself on Dunya when she is employed as a governess in his house

Marfa Petrovna Svidrigailov
his wife, who first accuses Dunya, and then publicly apologizes

Pyotr Petrovich Luzhin
Marfa Petrovna's cousin, a successful lawyer, with whom she arranged an engagement with Dunya

Andrei Semyonovich Lebezyatnikov
Luzhin's protégé and host in St. Petersburg; also the Marmeladov's landlord

THE MARMELADOV FAMILY PLOT

Semyon Marmeladov
a low-level government functionary, out of work because he drinks

Names

Russian novels are notable for their bewildering variety of names. Every character seems to be called something different by every other character, and all the names seem to mean something, but you can't tell what. The truth is a little simpler (though not much!)

Russians have three names: their given name, their patronymic, and their family name. The given name, like Rodion, can be made more intimate be shortening it to Rodya or Rodka. The patronymic explains the identity of someone's father. Romanovich means son of Roman; notice that Raskolnikov's sister has a different patronymic, Romanovna, which means daughter of Roman. Dostoyevsky, like Charles Dickens,

the great British writer of the same period, chose his family names because they had clear meanings to his readers, though those meanings can baffle modern and foreign readers. He called the drunken official Raskolnikov befriends Marmeladov because it means jelly; he's always wiggling out of his responsibilities. The name Svidrigailov was in fact familiar to Russians in the 1860's, because of a notorious country squire who, with the help of a trusted lackey, seduced and abused young girls. The name Raskolnikov invokes the word raskolnik, which means Old Believer, a member of large group of rural religious fanatics. Dostoyevsky chose the name to indicate that the novel is more the story of a crisis of faith, than of a murder.

Sofia Semyonovna Marmeladov
his daughter, forced into
prostitution by her father's
poverty

Katerina Ivanovna Marmeladov
his consumptive wife,
who does not love him

Polenka, Lenya and Kolya
her children from her first
marriage

**Amalia Ivanovna (or
Ludwigovna)**
the family's landlady, with
whom Katerina feuds

There are many other minor
characters, but they contribute
little to the plot

Plots

The Classics Illustrated
adaptation of *Crime and
Punishment* includes only
one of the plot lines of the
novel, the murder of the
pawn broker. Even that,
however, is narrowly represented.
Raskolnikov is portrayed as a
paranoid schizo-
phrenic with violent
tendencies, who mur-
ders for money and
then hides all he
steals under a stone.
He has no redeeming
qualities, and no kind-
ness, only despera-

tion. Only at the very end of this
adaptation, when he knows that
the police inspector Porfiry knows
that he is the murderer, does
Raskolnikov feel guilt for what he
has done. The punishment of the
title seems only to be his anxiety
about having his crime found out.

That isn't the way the novel
itself reads. Raskolnikov feels
guilty before and after the crime,
but does not
believe that
society has
any right to
punish him
for what he
has done.
The pawn-
broker, in his

estimation, is little more than a
louse, a parasite on the community. Killing her isn't a crime but a
service to society. Furthermore,
he has written an article which
argues in part that if civilization is
going to have its Napoleons and
its Galileos, it will have to accept
that those remarkable people will
not and cannot be constrained by
laws. Raskolnikov's murder of

the pawn broker is a sort of test, to find out if he is one of the geniuses to whom laws do not apply. At the end of the novel, he seems to conclude that society is irrelevant to him, not that he is above or outside its laws, but that those laws bear no relationship to him. The police are a worrisome inconvenience, nothing more. He enjoys toying with Zametov and even with Porfiry, though Porfiry is such a skilled investigator, and so adept at criminal psychology, that Raskolnikov fears him a little.

In the novel itself, the fact that Raskolnikov has murdered two people becomes a subtext—an underlying story—in the more pressing parts of his life. Even before he commits the murder, the two other plots of the novel are put in motion. First, Raskolnikov receives a letter from his mother explaining the trouble his sister Dunya has had with the Svidrigailovs, and how Marfa Petrovna made up for wrongfully accusing her by first publicly clearing her name, and then by arranging for her marriage to her well-to-do cousin Pyotr Petrovich Luzhin. Though his mother puts a happy face on this engagement, Raskolnikov sees that Dunya has sold herself to Luzhin in order to save their mother and Raskolnikov himself, who has abandoned not only school but the world around him. Still, her

brother can see plainly from his mother's letter that Luzhin wants a wife with no dowry so that he can control her through his money (in this way he is very much like Dostoyevsky's own father). Raskolnikov plans to stop this marriage.

Luzhin has come to St. Petersburg to pursue some business with the government and has arranged for Dunya and her mother to come as well, though he does not pay for their passage and rents them a wretched flat. When Luzhin comes to meet Raskolnikov — after the murders and after he has recovered a little from the delirium and fever which follow them — Raskolnikov insults and repels him, vowing to his face to break off this engagement. He quickly tells his mother and sister what he has done. His mother is desperate, but Dunya, who has already had her suspicions regarding Luzhin, wants only to test the truth of what her brother says.

Meanwhile, Raskolnikov has befriended Marmeladov in a bar. Marmeladov pours out his tales to his new friend: how (like Dostoyevsky and his first wife) Katerina had married him only because she was alone with small children, had tuberculosis, and had nowhere else to turn; how Katerina resents him for having brought her down from the high social position to which she was born; how Katerina first goaded Marmeladov's daughter Sonya into becoming a prostitute, and then fell at her feet in profound regret when Sonya returned home with money. Marmeladov says he does not drink to ease his pain, but rather to wallow in his misery. Raskolnikov sees his new friend home and meets Katerina and her children; the gentle and religious Sonya can no longer live with her father.

Then tragedy strikes: Marmeladov is crushed under a carriage. Raskolnikov happens to be nearby when this occurs — the coincidences in *Crime and Punishment* would be funny, if there didn't seem to be a thematic reason for them — and gives

Dostoyevsky's Crime

Feodor Dostoyevsky was not a murderer, but it seems possible that he had committed a crime, something far worse than the mild sort of revolutionary talk for which he was sent to prison. He is said to have confessed to Ivan Turgenev, another Russian writer who was his life-long rival, that he had once raped a small girl. Turgenev asked, "Why do you tell me this?" Dostoyevsky answered, "To show you how much I despise you." His friend and biographer Nikolay Strakhov said that of all the people in his fiction, Dostoyevsky was closest in personality to Svidrigailov. Throughout his fiction, he portrayed teenage and younger girls not only as objects of older men's desire, but as full of erotic desires themselves.

It is possible that Dostoyevsky only desired young girls and, delving into his own twisted psyche, wrote persuasively about that desire and the guilt he felt regarding it.

The portrait of Raskolnikov prob-ably embodies Dostoyevsky both as he was and as he hoped to be. The intensity, bordering on derange-ment, leads him to regard the evil Svidrigailov as a possible solution to his moral dilemma. His quest for a higher truth brings him to Sonya. But Raskolnikov is entirely devoid of sexuality of any kind. He acknowledges that his dead fiancee, his landlady's daughter, was ugly and that that was part of what he liked about her. Though he feels he has to choose between a libertine and a prostitute, Raskolnikov is openly disgusted by Svidrigailov's passion for young girls, and the closest he gets to Sonya is kissing the hem of her dress. It is fair to say that Dostoyevsky was hiding something about Raskolnikov's sexuality. It is possible that Raskolnikov's underlying crime is not so much murder as it is rape. He hides his axe under his coat and when he pulls it out he penetrates two women with it. It could be that *Crime and Punishment* was Dostoyevsky's disguised attempt to confess his past and reach the redemption Sonya offered Raskolnikov.

Katerina all of his money to pay for the funeral. Soon after, Sonya comes to Raskolnikov's apartment to thank him and to invite him to the funeral and the banquet afterwards; when she arrives, Dunya, Madame Raskolnikov, and Razumihin are all present, and yet Raskolnikov treats her with great respect despite her social shame. His mother suspects that Sonya is at the root of her son's peculiar behavior. Luzhin seems to confirm this by sending his fiancee and her mother a letter saying that Raskolnikov has shown them disrespect by allowing them to sit socially with a prostitute, and that he had given her all his money, not Katerina; he knows about Sonya because he lives in the same building as the Marmeladovs. He refuses to meet with Raskolnikov, which forces Dunya to choose between her brother and his future husband. She decides to test her brother's opinion of Luzhin by forcing a meeting between them. Luzhin becomes enraged and shows what a miserly manipulator he is. Dunya breaks off with him.

The Raskolnikovs' situation is not nearly so desperate as it seemed before, because yet another twist has appeared in the story in the form of Svidrigailov, the country squire who victimized Dunya when she was a governess in his house. His wife Marfa Petrovna has died suddenly—some say suspiciously—and Svidrigailov has returned to St. Petersburg to resume the life of gambling and seduction he had led before his marriage to Marfa Petrovna. He now has a small fortune to waste on his amoral pursuits, particularly the sexual corruption of young girls. He denies that Dunya is one of his targets. He visits Raskolnikov to inform him that he will bestow a sizable sum on Dunya to apologize for his past actions. Dunya and her mother now no longer need Luzhin. Unfortunately, this financial freedom means to Raskolnikov that they no longer need him, either.

As the novel drives toward its conclusion, the action begins to focus more on Sonya, the prostitute daughter of the dead Marmeladov. Raskolnikov sees in her — in her humble acceptance of her suffering — a possible answer to his deep questioning of faith. He challenges her, but her humility before God is unshakable. Even when Luzhin, in a desperate effort to prove to Dunya that her brother associates with thieves, plants a 100 ruble note on Sonya and then accuses her — at her father's funeral banquet, paid for with Raskolnikov's money — of stealing it, Sonya is shaken, but accepting of her fate. Only when Luzhin's old protégé

Lebezyatnikov says he witnessed Luzhin's deception is Sonya vindicated.

This final trial gives Raskolnikov faith, at least in Sonya. He follows her to her room, confesses to the murder of the pawnbroker, and begs for Sonya to guide him to redemption. Unfortunately, Svidrigailov, who has quarters in the Sonya's building, has overheard the confession and plans to use this knowledge to force Raskolnikov to help him win Dunya. Raskolnikov, indifferent to police authority, refuses to help Svidrigailov, who nonetheless tries to use his knowledge of the crime to blackmail Dunya into sleeping with him. She too refuses; she uses the gun she brought with her for protection to fend off Svidrigailov's attack.

Raskolnikov now believes he has two choices: either Sonya's humble acceptance of God or Svidrigailov's total amorality. That is, either there is a divine morality to which all people are subject (including the world's Napoleons and Galileos) or there is no God, in which case there is nothing, except the laws of an unjust society, to stop anyone from behaving just as he or she pleases. This is not always bad, as

IT WAS I WHO KILLED THE OLD PAWNBROKER WOMAN AND HER SISTER WITH AN AXE AND ROBBED THEM!

Raskolnikov knows; when Katerina Marmeladov, dies in the wake of her husbands funeral, Svidrigailov gives her children enough money to receive good care and an education. But Svidrigailov, destroyed by Dunya's refusal and haunted by a dream in which a five-year-old girl becomes a lascivious whore because of him, kills himself. Sonya, fallen as she is, is Raskolnikov's only answer. She tells him to confess his crime to the police and accept society's punishment; if he does that, she will follow him to Siberia, care for him, and love him until his faith returns. Hoping for this spiritual redemption, Raskolnikov confesses. Dunya and Razumihin, meanwhile, fall in love, marry, and agree to keep Mrs. Raskolnikov in the dark about Rodion's fate. The novel ends with Raskolnikov recovering his faith while in prison, exactly what happened to Dostoyevsky himself.

What Crime?
What Punishment?

You may notice that the foregoing description of the plot does not include much of the action included in the Classics Illustrated adaptation of *Crime and Punishment*. That is because this action takes place against the background of the murder story. Raskolnikov's dealings with the police are only inciden- tal to the main thrust of the novel, which has much more to do with portraying his deranged mind than with demon- strating how he hopes to outsmart Porfiry, the inspector. Porfiry and the police seem to be in the novel to serve two purposes. The first is to rep- resent civil authority: they are the people in charge of society, and in those rare moment when Raskolnikov associates with the civilized world, the police are always present. The second pur- pose, embodied in Porfiry, is to give legitimacy to the psychologi- cal concepts of self and personali- ty which compelled Dostoyevsky to write the novel in the first place. By putting psychologi- cal insights into the mouth of a well- educated, responsi-

ble and respected man, those insights and the many others Dostoyevsky contributes to the novel acquire a legitimacy they might not have if they came only from the author. It is important to realize that the police have noth- ing to connect Raskolnikov to the crime except that he was one of the pawnbroker's clients. He could walk away without punish- ment from society, but only at the cost of the redemption promised by Sonya. It is that hoped-for redemption, which he acquires only after a long struggle in prison, and not his guilt over committing the mur- ders, which drives him to confess. Raskolnikov suffers from a crisis of faith, and the murders are the physical manifestation of that cri- sis. The police themselves cannot affect what lies at the heart of Raskolnikov's trouble.

This raises an interesting ques- tion with the title of the novel: while it seems obvious what the crime is, it isn't quite so clear what the punishment is.

Raskolnikov cer- tainly suffers in the book. He is demented for a good part of the narrative, and when he isn't obviously insane, he is physically ill;

sweating through days of fever and delirium. Not only that, but he receives enough trauma for a lifetime in the course of the few weeks covered by the book. He comes to the rescue of his sister, he faces imprisonment for debt, a friend dies a violent and horrible death right before his eyes, and he is the obvious subject of police suspicion for the murders he committed. Still, none of these, except the last, can be seen as a punishment for his crimes. It is equally true that he receives no rewards for his crimes. The comic-book adaptation implies that Raskolnikov moves to new lodgings, and implies he bought clothes and went out to eat on his stolen money; in fact, he does all this with money sent from home.

So what does Dostoyevsky mean by using the word 'punishment' in the title? Note the time Raskolnikov spends in prison, which takes up only a few short pages at the end. In part,

BEHIND THE DOOR? LYING BEHIND THE DOOR? BEHIND THE DOOR?

Raskolnikov's self-recrimination is his punishment. He feels guilty and calls himself a louse. Because of these feelings, he separates himself from the people who could help him: his mother, his sister, Razumihin. But this is only a small part of what Raskolnikov suffers, and Dostoyevsky has purposely clouded how guilty Raskolnikov feels because he doesn't want readers to conclude that it is Raskolnikov's conscience which is punishing him. Raskolnikov makes it clear during his confession to Sonya that he doesn't regret having killed the pawn broker, so it is clear that a guilty conscience is not really what punishes him.

Dostoyevsky has a more profound point to make. He links crime with punishment not because Raskolnikov is going to be punished for his crime, but because the crime itself is a part of Raskolnikov's punishment. He is suffering for his ideas; he has fallen slave to his own mind. In explaining his murderous actions to his sister he says, "I do not understand why hurling bombs at people, according to

THE FOLLOWING DAY, THE STUDENT-MURDERER BOUGHT NEW CLOTHES, MOVED TO NEW LODGINGS AND DINED AT A FASHIONABLE RESTAURANT...

GIVE ME SOME TEA AND BRING ME THE PAPERS FOR THE LAST FIVE DAYS.

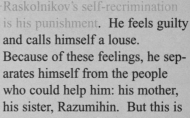

all the rules of warfare, is a more respectable form" of bloodshed. "Now more than ever I fail to understand my crime." Raskolnikov wants to transcend society, to put himself in a place where the rules governing civilized behavior no longer apply to him. This is a very revolutionary act, and it is an act, like most revolutions, which implies violence. He wants freedom and tries to achieve it by simply denying the power of authority over his life.

But Raskolnikov not only discards civil authority, he discards moral authority too. He makes the mistake of assuming that law equals morality, neglecting to realize that some sorts of morality transcend social authority and the law. He only discovers this error through Sonya, whose patient spirituality teaches him the limits and the usefulness of civil authority. The punishment Raskolnikov suffers is for this error. Once you realize that Dostoyevsky wants you to see the murders as punishment, you have to rethink what you believe he wants you to understand as crime. What seemed obvious at the beginning is not so obvious when you look at the book more carefully.

THEY DON'T HIDE THAT THEY ARE TRACKING ME LIKE A PACK OF DOGS. THEY SIMPLY SPIT IN MY FACE. COME, STRIKE ME OPENLY, DON'T PLAY WITH ME LIKE A CAT WITH A MOUSE. AND WHAT IF IT'S ONLY MY FANCY?

REALITY

While reality is the most interesting and complex theme in the book, Dostoyevsky develops several others too, one intimately connected with the first. His concern with Raskolnikov's interior life — Marmeladov and Svidrigailov receive similar though less probing treatment as well — leaves the nature of reality in doubt. Since he is portraying a mind and not a world, states have more importance than objects and dreams have more relevance than actions. Raskolnikov points to this very problem himself when he wakes from a dream to find Svidrigailov standing in his doorway. "Can this be a continuation of my dream?" he asks himself. Depending on how you take the question, the answer could easily be yes. In many ways, *Crime and Punishment* is more a long narrative dream than a conventional novel. Rather than individuals whose live and emotions we enter, the book presents its characters as people who relate to one another much as symbols in a dream do.

Unlike most novels, *Crime and Punishment* tries more to represent a state of mind than an objective reality. What makes the book so important is that it tells a great story, with compelling characters, at the same time it implies that the characters are only there to flesh out Dostoyevsky's ideas. He has accomplished something very tricky, and when thinking or talking about the book one has to be constantly aware that Dostoyevsky is not only representing the lives of his characters but also the complex state of a mind deprived of clear moral values.

Except when Dostoyevsky makes it clear that he is most concerned with Raskolnikov's state of mind (as at the beginning of Part Six when he writes "it was as if fog suddenly fell around him and confined him in a hopeless and heavy solitude" during which "he would consider something to be the consequence of an event that existed only in his imagination") Raskolnikov's world does have an objective reality. He lives in a wretched, run-down little hole. The people he meets are described in detail. The street scenes in particular are so convincingly rendered the reader can almost smell the stench of 19th-century St. Petersburg.

But Dostoyevsky throws in small facts which make the reader doubt the novel's objective reality, things that make it seem that he is only concerned with the theoretical relationships between the ideas his people represent. For example, it is very peculiar that Luzhin, a successful lawyer, lives in the same building, or even the same part of town, as the struggling Marmeladovs. If one coincidence of this sort is not enough to introduce doubt about the nature of *Crime and Punishment's* reality, Dostoyevsky also places the wealthy Svidrigailov not just in the same building with the prostitute Sonya, but in the next room. Further, people seldom fail to find the people they are looking when they go in search of them. Only Raskolnikov seems to make a habit of absenting himself when people want him, but that could be just another suggestion that he is not meant to be taken as a completely real person.

This partial rendering of reality exactly suits Dostoyevsky's purpose, since he is only partially interested in telling a good yarn about fascinating people. By presenting Raskolnikov's existence as only vaguely real, he makes both his psychological exploration and his philosophical concerns seem that much more urgent. The reality of *Crime and Punishment* is the reality of a state of mind, in which the details give weight and continuity to the world in which that state of mind exists. If Dostoyevsky had made his book completely about Raskolnikov's internal life, it would have had less power. The problem Raskolnikov wants to solve is how to transcend society. Dostoyevsky uses the form of his novel to reply that it can't be done.

DUALITY

From his title onward, Dostoyevsky has organized *Crime and Punishment* as a series of dualities: Raskolnikov moves from pride to humility, from reason to faith, from isolation to community. As a part of this structure, Dostoyevsky includes pairs of characters, people who represent alternative ideas, or even mirror versions of the same idea. For example, Raskolnikov chooses between Sonya's transcendent morality and Svidrigailov's debased amorality. Some paired characters have ideological connections (Marmeladov and Luzhin) and others, emotional ones (the pawnbroker and Raskolnikov's mother).

The structure of the novel as a whole has the same duality. The first half of the book retells Raskolnikov's struggle to achieve darkness and isolation; the second explores his attempt to find redemption and communion.

This duality, balances both the structure of the book and the characters in it, moving forward a story which could otherwise be static and immobile.

Study Questions

• How would you answer Raskolnikov's hypothesis that certain people cannot be obligated to follow the laws of society?

• Though he is hungry, poor and desperate, Raskolnikov buries not only the pawn broker's pledges, which may be traceable, but also her cash, which is not. Why would he do this?

• The Classics Illustrated adaptation of *Crime and Punishment* was first published in 1951. Can that time of publication explain anything about why the adaptation omits Sonya, the prostitute, Svidrigailov, the profligate, and many other morally questionable characters?

• What does Razumihin see in Raskolnikov that makes him work so hard for him, despite the abuse his friend heaps on him and madness he seems to embrace? Why does Razumihin like Raskolnikov so much?

• Is Raskolnikov insane? How can you tell?